Logan Clendening Lectures on the
History and Philosophy of
Medicine

Fourth Series

Leonardo the Anatomist

Logan Clendening Lectures on the History and
Philosophy of Medicine

Fourth Series

Leonardo the Anatomist

by

Elmer Belt, M.D.

**GREENWOOD PRESS, PUBLISHERS
NEW YORK**

CONTENTS

I

Leonardo da Vinci's Technical Innovations and Discoveries in Anatomy

I. Leonardo da Vinci's Technical Innovations and Discoveries in Anatomy

"This my illustration of the human body shall be demonstrated to you, not otherwise than if you had a real man before you."   *Quaderni I, 2 r.*

In his early youth as a student of art in Verrocchio's *bottega* in Florence, Leonardo learned the anatomy of flayed bodies. This was topographical anatomy, the study of the underlying structures which mold the human form, a study of great use to the artist.[1]

But for Leonardo the study of anatomy became a science. In it he combined the study of structure, revealed through his quick eye and through his habit of precise artistic portrayal, with a study of function. He never did separate structure from function in his thinking.

This treatment of anatomy as a science and its demonstration in accurate drawings were an innovation. Scientific demonstration of structure and function before Leonardo was limited to the repetitious use of five or six schematic pictures seen endlessly recurring with only slight modifications since antiquity. Botanical illustration, too, consisted of a static description of the plant and its parts. In Leonardo's botanical drawings the plant can be seen striving, living, growing.

In Leonardo's drawings of the human body man lives, functions, changes. Leonardo, the artist, renders these human figures in their most subtle spiritual expression. He succeeds, too, in showing the human form in quick motion, in violent motion, and in dramatic emotion. Behind all this is correct dynamic anatomy. All depends upon the correct depiction of the functioning human frame. The use of the limbs and their working are to him a mechanical performance worthy of deep study. Leonardo's insatiable desire to know and his penetrating intelligence converted Leonardo the Artist into a Scientist now traveling along unexplored roads.

As Leonardo progressed in his anatomic studies he realized that his investigation must comprise the study of the body from babyhood to old age and must include even a study of the foetus in its various stages. His general plan for this anatomy was to study each part, from the bones outward to the skin, presenting four views in rotation of each part and in the case of the bones, in addition to these four views, a cross-section and a longitudinal section.[2]

At the end of his work when he was an old man living in Clos Lucé in France he told De Beatis, who visited his studio, that in his lifetime he had dissected thirty bodies.[3] The evidence shows that he also studied the bodies of animals, including pigs in the slaughterhouse immediately after they were killed. His favorite animal for anatomic study was the ox.

Leonardo studied the traditional texts of his day in manuscripts and printed books, such as those of Avicenna, Albertus Magnus, Albertus of Saxony, Benedetti, and the Galenic writings interpreted by Mundinus. He absorbed these works so well that he often contradicted the authors in his notes as if they were his living contemporary adversaries. In his later years he had access to Galen's *De usu partium* which, in the sections he needed, was doubtless translated for him by his friends. We know from his notes that he used the libraries San Marco and Santo Spiritu in Florence, the Visconti Sforza Library in Pavia, and the Sforza Library in Pesaro.[4]

Among Leonardo's contemporaries, also keenly interested in anatomy, were Pollaiuolo and Verrocchio. For a short period, 1510 to 1511, the physician Marcantonio della Torre may have been his associate at this work, but unfortunately Marcantonio della Torre died at the age of thirty while ministering to victims of the Bubonic Plague. In this year Leonardo was fifty-eight years old. Their association, if it existed, could have lasted only a few months.

Two of Leonardo's anatomic studies are dated. One of these is the leaf showing the front and lateral views of the skull and the vessels of the forehead, *Fogli B, 42 r.*, which carries the date 1489, when Leonardo was 37. The large leaf, *Fogli A, 17 r.*, with the drawing of the foot and leg, is dated 1510. These dated figures are only roadmarks. Leonardo's entire work in anatomy extends beyond these dates in both directions, probably from 1472 to 1513, comprising fifty-one years of observation and study.

In his notes Leonardo tells of dissecting in the hospital of Santa Maria Nuova in Florence.[5] He also may have participated in the public dissections in Santa Croce which, according to the diary of the shopkeeper Landucci, took place in Florence in January of 1505. Leonardo is known to have dissected in the hospital Santo Spiritu in Rome. He records having had to discontinue his work in this hospital when the "German deceiver," the mirror-maker Giovanni, who had been assigned by the Pope to help him, "hindered him in anatomy."[6]

The Records of Leonardo's Anatomic Studies

"Leonardo da Vinci disciple of experience."

Codex Atlanticus, 191 r. a.

Leonardo often stated that experience in anatomy can be obtained only by dissection. "Chisel and bone saw, and the sharp knife" which Leonardo lists so often in his memoranda of equipment had to be combined with the dual gift of recording pictorially and in words what he had seen, in order to give his anatomic researches that degree of realism which makes them seem modern today.

Leonardo often explains the advantage of pictorial over merely verbal demonstration. In his statement on anatomic demonstration,[7] he points out the advantage of being able to show in one drawing the observations made in various figures, and in *Quaderni II*, 1 r., he states: "With what words, O writer, can you with like perfection describe the whole arrangement of that of which the design is here? ... How in words can you describe this heart without filling a whole book? Yet the more detail you write concerning it, the more you will confuse the mind of the hearer."

Although Leonardo emphasizes pictorial description his own word-descriptions are remarkable for their clarity

6

and brevity, which is in marked contrast to the involved "scientific prose" of his contemporaries. Contemporary prose, such as that of Luca Pacioli, was involved and overloaded with references.[8] Leonardo ranks among the first and perhaps the best of scientific prose writers. His prose is functional and matter-of-fact but still has an inimitable rhythm. Leonardo is always an artist even in his prose record of scientific observations. He fills the dry record of anatomic description with apt and enlivening comparisons.

Preservation of Leonardo's Records

"Worthy of memory is Leonardo da Vinci, who taught the anatomy of the human body and of the horse. I have seen these divine drawings by his hand at Francesco Melzi's."

Gian Paolo Lomazzo, *Idea del Tempio della Pittura.* Milan, 1590.

Leonardo's notebooks cover a period of forty-five years of his life. He carried them with him when he left Italy for France in 1516. De Beatis, secretary to the Cardinal d'Aragon, in 1517 wrote in his personal record of having been shown by Leonardo at Amboise in France "a particular treatise of anatomy with demonstrations in draft not only of the members but also of the muscles, nerves, veins, joints, intestines, and of whatever can be reasoned about in the bodies of both men and women in a way that has never been done by any other person." Leonardo, he reports, said he had dissected thirty bodies. "Altogether," De

Beatis continues, "an endless number of volumes written in the vulgar tongue which if they are ever published will be both profitable and very delectable."[3] Many years were to pass before in our day these *still* delectable and profitable books were finally to be published.

After Leonardo's death in 1519, Leonardo's heir, Francesco Melzi, removed Leonardo's scientific manuscripts to his villa in Vaprio d'Adda. Upon Francesco Melzi's death in 1570 they passed to his nephew, the lawyer Orazio Melzi, who did not realize their worth. Because of his carelessness some were stolen by his children's tutor, a young man named Lelio Gavardi d'Asola, and some were given away. General popular interest in these manuscripts finally made Orazio Melzi aware of their monetary value. He recovered much of the manuscript material he had permitted to become disseminated and then sold it to the sculptor, Pompeo Leoni.[9] While Pompeo Leoni had these manuscripts he showed them to Rubens in Italy between 1601 and 1606. Rubens appreciated and described their great beauty.[10]

Pompeo Leoni carried all the Leonardo drawings in his possession to Spain, with the idea of presenting them to King Philip, but Philip died before he could present them to him. He brought back some of them to Italy; the rest were left in Spain. There, in 1638, they were purchased from a Spanish owner by Thomas Howard, Earl of Arundel, and were taken to England.

The first notice that they were in the possession of the

English crown is found in notes sent to Cassiano del Pozzo by Luigi Arconati in 1639.[11] The mode of transfer from Arundel to the Crown of these materials is unknown. It is said that King Charles I himself had placed the Vincian drawings in a large and strong chest. Reference to them appears again in 1690, when they were shown to Huygens by Queen Mary II of England. Huygens stated that they were kept in a chest which also contained a packet of drawings by Holbein. We have no record that they were seen again until they were found by a librarian, Robert Dalton, in Kensington Castle in a locked chest, the key to which had been lost. They were still stored with the Holbein drawings. Dalton's rediscovery occurred about 1760, early in the reign of King George III. Dalton showed Leonardo's drawings to Dr. William Hunter, who described them to his students. In his lecture, Dr. Hunter told the students they were 300 years ahead of their time. He mentioned the possibility of publishing them himself.[12]

In the winter of 1751, Dr. Hunter had his first favorable opportunity to examine the placenta of a human being. Before that time he had studied the placenta in animals, but he awaited with eagerness the opportunity for a first-hand study of the human placenta. Hunter stated: "A woman died suddenly when very near the end of her pregnancy; the body was procured before any sensible putrefaction had begun, the season of the year was favorable to dissection; the injection of blood-vessels proved successful; a very able painter in this way was found; every part was examined in the most public manner and the truth was thereby well authenticated."[13] In this statement one can almost hear Leonardo describing his own experience. When Robert Dalton showed Dr. Hunter Leonardo's drawings, Hunter must have been especially impressed with the drawing of the foetus *in utero,* for here, for the first time in the history of science, the correct foetal position is shown within the uterus and the separateness of the foetal circulatory components within the placenta from those of the maternal circulation is seen; the cotyledons of the foetal side are demonstrated as interdigitating with projections from the maternal portion of the placenta "like the fingers of one hand placed between the digits of the other," to paraphrase Leonardo's clarifying simile. Hunter's Atlas of the gravid uterus was in progress when he saw Leonardo's drawings and was published in 1774. So it is easy to appreciate Hunter's urgent desire to publish these beautiful studies of Leonardo. Hunter also brought the Leonardo drawings to the attention of Blumenbach of Göttingen, the founder of the science of anthropology. Blumenbach wrote about the drawings in 1788.[14] Hunter had died in 1783 and therefore did not live to see their first publication. They first appeared in part in Chamberlaine's volume published in 1796. These first engravings were by Bartolozzi. Very few publications of Leonardo's anatomic dissections followed this initial volume. A reprint of Bartolozzi's erroneous depiction of Leonardo's copulation drawing was published in *Tabula Anatomica,* Lüneburg, 1830, and proved very popular with art and medical students.

With the development of reproduction processes many facsimile editions of Leonardo's work were made. The anatomic drawings are now accessible in three such publications: *Dell' Anatomia Fogli A,* Paris, 1892, and *Dell' Anatomia Fogli B,* Torino, 1901, both edited by Sabachnikoff and Piumati; *Quaderni d'Anatomia communicazioni dell' Istituto Anatomico dell' Universita di Christiania,* six volumes published annually from 1911 to 1916. In the latest facsimile edition *Leonardo on the Human Body,* New York, Schuman, 1952, the editors, Charles O'Malley and J. B. de C. M. Saunders, have attempted to group the Windsor anatomical drawings chronologically and to give a new evaluation of Leonardo's achievements in anatomy.[15]

At the present time there are 600 original drawings in Windsor Castle. When they were counted at the time of Dalton's rediscovery there were 779. This lost anatomic treasure of 179 drawings may some day be found. One fugitive leaf in the Museum in Weimar, Germany, may belong to this lost group. It contains beautiful demonstrations of the brain, the spinal nerves, and the optic chiasma. On the opposite side are important drawings of, and remarks on, the reproductive organs.[16]

Study by Dissection

"Spectacles with cardboard, steel and fork, and

11

bistoury, charcoal, drawing board and sheets of paper and pencil and pipe clay and wax, thongs and quarrel, small-toothed bone saw, chisel, ink stand, penknife. . . ." *Quaderni I,* Folio 13 v.

Leonardo describes dissection by morselment, removing little by little minute portions of adventitious material from the vicinity of special structures under study within the body, preparing the exposed material left behind for demonstration and for sketching, much as is done today. No method of artificial preservation of the anatomic material thus under study is mentioned. Leonardo does mention the difference and ease of dissection of the dry thin bodies of those of great age as compared to the fat succulent bodies of the young.

It is a joy to see his progress from early diagrams, which he made to illustrate the word descriptions of Avicenna, to his later scientific anatomic drawings made from his own observations, accurately portraying the material he actually saw and dissected himself. "If you want to know thoroughly the parts of a dissected person, you must turn him or your eye, examining him from different aspects, from below, from above, and from the sides, turning him and investigating the origin of each member, and in this way the natural dissection satisfied you as to your knowledge. . . . Accordingly, through my design, every part and every whole will be known to you by means of the demonstration of three different aspects of each part."[17]

The purpose of Leonardo's drawings was to reveal structure and sometimes function through visual demonstrations of the actually dissected material. He said that he combined in each single drawing the experience gained from a number of dissections. He found ingenious ways of demonstration never used before to show simultaneously in one drawing not only what he had experienced in various dissections but also the various layers of the dissected specimen which could not be shown in a straight surface view. He thus maintained the characteristics of a study from nature. He seldom used diagrams. An instance of such use is the drawing of the frog's spinal cord.[18] In another diagram he shows the rotation of radius in the forearm by the biceps and pronator teres muscles. He drew the entire body in anterior, lateral, and posterior projections as if he were walking around the dissection.

In Leonardo's bones a lifelike portrayal is given to all of his pictures through the presentation of proper carrying and supporting angles which are correctly shown, thus creating realism even in his skeletal drawings. Leonardo illustrated every bone in the body. He demonstrated the actions of the bones as levers when acted upon by muscles. He illustrated for the first time the proper double curvature of the spine, the true tilt of the pelvis, and the proper number of vertebrae, accurately portraying each, especially those of the cervical spine and sacrum.[19]

He described the teeth, presenting their proper number, strangely a matter of dispute,[20] for as Vesalius a gen-

13

Diagram of the spinal cord and vertebral canals with notes on the paralyzing effect of pithing a frog. *Qu. V*, 21 r.

The vascular pattern presented as if the leg were transparent. *Qu.V*, 3 v.

14

eration later said: "Anyone can count his own teeth." Demonstrating the antra in the skull he shows the upward projection of the teeth of the upper jaw into the floor of the maxillary sinus.

He was the first accurately to show the bones of the hand. He said that he had observed twenty-seven sesamoid bones, and he presented the mechanical principles by which these bones function.[21]

Leonardo stated that it was necessary to saw all bones longitudinally and also in cross-section in order properly to study their structure. Thus in sectioning the skull he discovered the spaces within the bones of the skull known as sinuses and demonstrated for the first time the maxillary sinus or the antrum of Highmore and the teeth of the upper jaw which enter it.[22]

Leonardo's mediums and drawing techniques differ. It is most likely that drawings executed with the same medium on the same type of paper can be dated as belonging to the same period. Leonardo used silverpoint on coated paper with a unique sharpness and conciseness of line, at the same time subtle and sensitive. He also used black and red chalk on more-or-less rough paper. The drawings of the heart in *Quaderni II*, chalk on greenish-blue very rough paper, stand out as a series, dated by Kenneth Clark as 1513. In the pen-and-ink drawing of *Fogli A*, folio 17 r., carrying the date 1510, there is corroborating evidence of Leonardo's style of this period.[23]

As visual aids Leonardo used rope strands to indicate

the direction, origin, and attachment of muscles.[24] He realized that in the body muscle groups are balanced, an anterior group against a posterior group, and he ingeniously used cord and wire in diagrams to represent muscle groups as a means of clarifying their action. This is the first use of this method of illustration in the history of anatomy.

Leonardo presented drawings as seeming transparencies.[25] This method of showing several layers of organic structure as if transparent with an overall outline of the parts removed in dissection, ingeniously anticipates modern principles of didactic demonstration. At an age when X-rays were not known and not even dreamt of, Leonardo's power of imagination seems miraculous. In the famous drawing of the legs he indicates (or identifies) for the first time in the history of anatomy the correct position of the femur.[26] Add to this discovery the quality of the drawing as such, a masterpiece of clearness and beauty of line, of distinctness, elegance, and dignity of form, and you have the artistic and scientific phenomenon: Leonardo at his best.

Leonardo was the first to depict cross-section anatomy.[27] Here again he used the principle of simultaneously showing in the pictorial demonstration what the eye is not able to discern at one glance. The surface of each cross-section is shown within the contour of the limb from which it is taken.

In Leonardo's studies of the complicated structures of

16

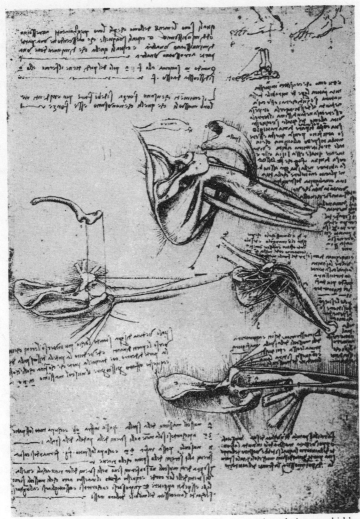

Figures with guide lines to demonstrate the anatomic relation to hidden deeper structures. *An. A.*, 2 r., *ca.* 1510.

the shoulder girdle[28] and in studies of the bones of the foot, he used exploded views with guide lines to indicate the source of the elevated structures, another innovation now often used to illustrate the relation of parts in complicated machinery. Equally ingenious were his glass models of the heart to show the action of the valves.[29] These were three-dimensional objects for demonstration, similar to those used today.

Comparative Anatomy and Use of Animal Specimens and Animal Experiments

"Man. The description of man, in which is contained those who are almost of the same species such as the baboon, the ape and others. . . . Lion and its followers, such as panthers, lions, tigers, leopards, lynxes. . . . Horse and its followers such as the mule, the ass and the like which have teeth above and below. . . . Bull and its followers which are horned and without upper teeth, such as buffalo. . . ."   *An. B,* 13 r.

In the course of his studies of the horse Leonardo was struck with the similarity of the muscles of the horse's hind leg and those of the lower extremity of man. He recognized, too, that the essential difference in appearance is that the horse stands on his great toe.[30] He also noted essential resemblances between the human leg and that of the horse and of the frog, and he left a careful record of his dissections of the foot and lower leg of a bear.[31]

18

He studied the anatomy of the bat with great care, drawing particularly its wings, for he needed these data for his labors on flight. The wings of birds, too, were carefully studied. During this study he became the first to recognize the bastard wing, or alula, attached to the thumb.[32]

In spite of his realization of the great differences among species, as well as their similarities, he does not bother to indicate by label the species of specimens he has so carefully drawn as "ox," "horse," or "dog," but he seems to assume in his text that the structures are the same for purposes of study. Actually in the great sheet of drawings of the larynx, a dog's or pig's thyroid and a dog's larynx are placed in the throat of a man.[33] In the magnificent drawing of the foetus *in utero* the uterus is that of a cow, and the typical ungulate placenta is shown in the drawing without a word of comment in the text regarding this mixture of species.[34]

Important Innovations and Discoveries

Leonardo experimented with animals,—for the most part they were cadavers,—but these animal experiments led him to some of his most important discoveries. Leonardo pithed a frog's spinal column, and thereby was able to describe the abolition of the frog's spinal reflexes.[35] He inflated and then forcibly deflated the lung of a goose, producing the characteristic goose "honk," in a study of the mechanism of the voice.[36] He studied the pierced hearts of pigs in Tuscany at their slaughter, demonstrating by this means the coincidence of three events: the pulse wave in the arteries, the beat of the heart against the chest wall, and the systolic contraction of the heart. His conclusions were a tremendous departure from the established opinion of his day.[37]

In the muscular system Leonardo suggested a system of nomenclature[38] for the muscles which would use a separate name for each muscle, a name designed to express its origin, insertion, direction of pull, and purpose. He defined for each separate muscle an individual innervation, individual blood supply, separate origin, insertion, and purpose.

He classified muscles as (1) those beginning in a cord and ending in a cord, a) with flat attachment, b) with a round attachment; (2) those with the cord only at one end, a) expanded, b) round; (3) compound muscles, those with two heads, their special value being that if one head is injured the other will take over its function.

It is noteworthy that this problem of organized nomenclature is still today foremost in the minds of anatomists. At the International Congress of Anatomists held at Oxford in the summer of 1950, the Congress resolved to set up a committee comprising three members from each of the countries or groups of countries represented. The committee was to arrange for an agreed International Anatomical Nomenclature to be presented for action to the Congress to be held in 1955 in France. Thus 500 years after Leonardo, his dream of a uniform meaningful anatomic nomenclature may be realized.

20

Leonardo identified the muscles of the face.[39] He described the action of muscles in general as a pulling action, the muscle using its force to pull along the line of its length. The exceptions to this pulling action were the tongue and penis, which push.[40] He stated that muscles do not move the member to which they are fixed at their origin but that they move it at their point of insertion, to which the sinew which leaves the muscle is attached. He also stated that muscular movement is by a continuous infinity of successive phases of motion. He indicated that posture is maintained by a constant interplay of reciprocally antagonistic muscles. He described the deltoid[41] as a separate muscle and stated that the pectoralis minor had as its primary action an accessory muscle of respiration pulling upward upon the rib cartilages.

He illustrated the biceps as being the chief supinator of the forearm, showing that it is only secondarily a flexor; he also showed that the pronator teres is its antagonist in action to pronate the arm. He described the restriction of rotation of the forearm with the arm in flexion as having a radius of one-half a circle while in extension three-fourths of a circle can be effected.[42] He stated that four muscles control the action of the eye.[43] He identified the heart as a muscle and, following his own criteria, searched for a nerve supply to this muscle, finally deciding upon the left branch of the vagus as the nerve of the heart.[44]

21

The Heart and the Blood. First Studies of Abnormalities of Gerontology[45]

"Of the heart. This moves of itself and does not stop unless forever. . . . Marvellous instrument, invented by the supreme Master."   *An. B*, 12 r.

In his discussion of the heart Leonardo was the first to state that it is composed of muscle; he was the first to describe it as being four-chambered. The two-chambered heart was an Aristotelian concept passed on by Avicenna and Mundinus. Leonardo saw and drew the auricles correctly, depicting them as receiving chambers for the peripheral blood. He maintained this idea in his descriptions and showed it in his drawings. He thought of the heart muscle as being layered instead of coiled, but he described and showed the attachment of the papillary muscles to the edge of the valve leaves and attached the cardiac muscle to the valve rings in a most modern fashion. Harvey was the first to boil the heart and unroll it. In this way Harvey showed that the heart was a continuous muscle. This point Leonardo missed.

Leonardo described the moderator band within the heart. He saw that the heart had to have its own blood and nerve supply in order to qualify, within his definition, as a muscle. He presented the left branch of the vagus as the nerve of the heart and worked out the coronary circulation in a series of studies which he presents in his drawings with an exquisite clearness, both in text and in drawing.

22

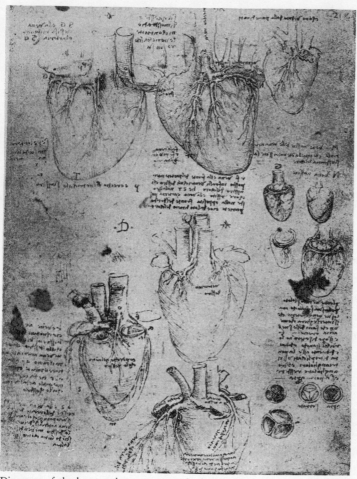

Diagrams of the heart and coronary vessels showing how the coronary arteries receive their blood from the aortic valve during diastole. *Qu. II*, 4 r., *ca.* 1513.

His concept of the movement of the blood was unfortunately too much influenced by his knowledge of Galen's *De usu partium*. From this work he accepted the incorrect notion that the interventricular septum was perforate. Thus these perforations could permit the blood to flow through the septum from the right side of the heart to the left, but Leonardo describes these channels as "invisible pores." He draws the mouth of one of them. In the supporting text surrounding this drawing he makes it clear that only the mouth is visible. It was impossible for him to follow the rest of the channel by dissection. It must be remembered that Harvey in his great opus which proved that the blood moves in a circle also had to assume the presence of invisible channels in the periphery which he could not see and through which the blood was conveyed from the arteries to the veins throughout the tissues of the body. Harvey thus had to presume the existence of capillaries. Their actual discovery awaited Leeuwenhoek's microscope and Malpighi's application of this instrument to the study of the capillary bed and the movement of the blood through it from artery to vein.

Leonardo, however, described the blood vessels of the body as constantly diminishing by division to the size of a hair, and he was the first to use the word "capillary" to describe these hairlike structures, too fine to see.

Like Harvey in his study of the action of the heart Leonardo applied mathematics to the problem of the amount of blood passing from the right auricle into the right ventricle. Unfortunately he left this task uncompleted, realizing only that the amount was a "great weight."

To Leonardo the motion of the heart and of the blood through it engendered body heat by friction. The blood he thought worked itself to a high temperature in the heart by beating against the endocardial structures and was cooled by its passage through the lungs and as it moved to the body's periphery.

Friction, Leonardo knew from his experiments in physics, could produce heat to the point of smoke, fire, and flame. He noted that in fevers the pulse grew rapid as the patient became burning hot. Thus the "vital spirits" of the Galenists, engendered by whipping up the blood with air in the right side of the heart, Leonardo rationalized into body heat attained through friction. But whence *does* come body heat? The cold-blooded crocodile and the shark, larger and stronger than man, burn oxygen and expend gigantic energy with no rise in temperature above that of their environment.

Leonardo's own experimental studies showing that no air could pass from the trachea to the right heart through lung and pulmonary vein and his own studies of the vital spirit in air consumed by the burning candle which in burning rendered the air unfit to sustain animal life were thus left at loose ends through lack of correlation of these facts. This failure to discover the circulation of the blood and the blood's use of the air drawn into the lungs was partly due to his lack of time but probably more especially to the lack of men of similar interest with whom this lonely intellectual giant could discuss and clarify by attrition with like minds his original studies and discoveries.

Leonardo believed that the blood surged in pulses from both ventricles of the heart, spending its force and its heat as the pulse wave moved on to the periphery. Arteries and veins both carried the blood on this outward journey. The arteries carried vital spirits, the veins carried nutriment. Thus to prevent the too easy escape of these readily diffusible vital spirits, the arteries must be thicker lest they be ruptured by the strain and the valves in the veins were there to slow the outward rush of blood and help its diffusion into the tissues. As each pulse wave subsided, the blood surged back except for the part lost in use. It surged back into the auricles and through them passed between the edges of the leaves of the valves of the heart into the ventricles again for another pulse. Like sound and light this pulsing force too was lost as it extended into the periphery. But Leonardo knew that age brought a change in the blood vessels,[46] a change-in their thickness, their length, the character of their inner surface, and the caliber of their lumen, all of which brought about a constriction in the lumen of the vessels. He ascribed to this occlusion the changes he saw in the periphery in the aged, stating clearly that because of the lack of the flow of blood, impeded because of the narrowing and twisting of the blood vessels, these parts suffered from malnutrition. He suggested also that sudden death in the aged might be due to the failure of the blood supply to the heart because of the thickening and narrowing of the blood vessels which supplied the musculature of the heart.

Speaking of "the old man" who died quietly while Leonardo was conversing with him at his bedside in the hospital Leonardo states: "And when I opened the body in order to ascertain the cause of so peaceful a death, I found that it proceeded from weakness through failure of blood and of the artery that feeds the heart and the other lower members, which I found to be parched and shrunk and withered; and the result of this autopsy I wrote down very carefully and with great ease, for the body was devoid of either fat or moisture, and these form the chief hindrance to the knowledge of its parts. The other autopsy was on a child of two years, and here I found everything the contrary to what it was in the case of the old man. The old who enjoy good health die through lack of sustenance. And this is brought about by the passage to the mesaraic veins becoming continually restricted by the thickening of the skin of these veins; and the process continues until it affects the capillary veins, which are the first to close up altogether."[47]

These observations make Leonardo the father of a modern branch of medicine: gerontology. It is noteworthy how often the motif of young versus old appears in Leonardo's drawings. The mystery of the circle of young and

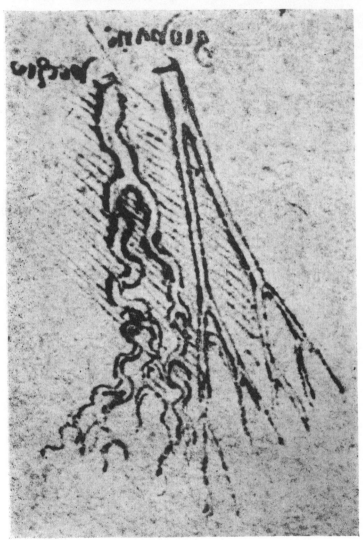

Blood vessels of the old and the young. *An. B*, 10 r.

old figures surrounding the Virgin in the unfinished painting of the Adoration in Florence presented a scientific problem to Leonardo to be investigated through experiment and dissection.

His dissection of the old man yielded him a large number of pathologic findings associated with arteriosclerosis, the significance of which he did not fail to point out. "The artery and the vein which in the old extend between the spleen and the liver, acquire so great a thickness of skin that it contracts the passage of the blood that comes from the mesaraic veins, through which this blood passes over to the liver and the heart and the two greater veins, and as a consequence through the whole body; and apart from the thickening of the skin these veins grow in length and twist themselves after the manner of a snake, and the liver loses the humour of the blood which was carried there by this vein; and consequently this liver becomes dried up and grows to be like frozen bran both in color and substance."[48]

The Lung

"When you represent the lung make it seem semi-transparent so it may not hide what is behind it, and let the semi-transparent part be all the ramifications of the trachea and the veins of the artery [aorta] and of the vena cava and then outside these draw a contour line around about them, to show the true shape, position and extent of this lung."

Quaderni III, 10 r.

29

We do not have many of Leonardo's studies of the lungs. The pillow-like softness of the lung tissue is described. In a series of experiments he inflated the lungs and then forcibly expelled the air from the lungs to show that no direct passage for air from the lung into the heart exists, and he also forcefully contracted the lungs in order to attempt to produce the voice. The latter maneuver he found effective in the goose, which possesses a syrinx. Leonardo did not locate the voice in the larynx. He correctly describes the action of swallowing and the fate of a bolus of food as it passes over the larynx into the esophagus.[49] He also describes the action of the intercostal muscles in respiration. He realizes the function of vacuum in the pleural space to keep the lungs against the chest wall during expansion of the chest cavity in respiration.[50] He carried out lifelong studies of the simple phenomenon of the exhausion of a vital principle in the air by the flame of a candle[51] as it burns in air inclosed within a drinking glass inverted over a dish of water. He states that in such exhausted burned air animals cannot live. He performed simple experiments to demonstrate the control of the act of breathing and discussed the function of the diaphragm and its share in that act.

The Nerves

"You should attend well to these reversive nerves and similarly to the other nerves because the movement of all the muscles springs from these nerves which with their ramifications pour themselves into these muscles." *Quaderni IV, 7* r.

Leonardo identified the nervous structure as a complete and related system, the brain substance being continuous with the nerves, the nerves extending to the periphery and carrying both motor action and sense perception. He adhered to authority in believing that a nerve to a muscle becomes, within the muscle, the connective tissue of that muscle, emerging as the tendon. He thus used the word *"nervi"* both for nerve and tendon, confusing these two structures in his notes and in his mind. He identified the spinal cord as the center of reflex life. "The tendons with their muscles serve the nerves even as soldiers serve their leaders, and to the nerves serve the common sense as the leaders their captain, and this common sense serves the soul as the captain serves his lord" (*An. B, 2* r.).

How are impulses carried through the nerves? To Leonardo the fluid within the ventricles of the brain, transporting impulses to and fro through minutely hollow nerves, seemed to be the answer. Hence the study of the ventricles, their shape and their fluid content, was all-important. Authority located the five senses within them. Leonardo met with great skill the anatomic problem presented by his desire to demonstrate these spaces within the soft brain.[52] It was the skill of a sculptor trained in the making of bronze figures. In using hot wax which he poured down into the ventricles through a hollow straw to fill these spaces while the fluid from the ventricles es-

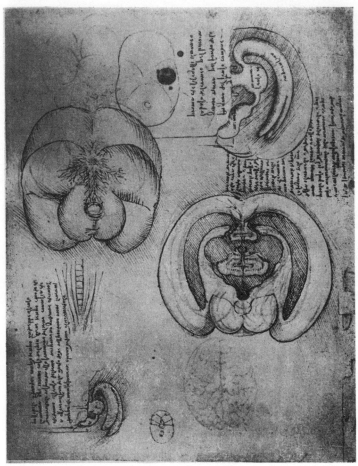

In the first anatomic use of a solidifying injection mass to demonstrate a body cavity Leonardo revealed the form of the ventricles of an ox brain. *Qu. V*, 7 r., *ca.* 1504.

caped through another lower opening, he followed a century-old method familiar to all workers in bronze: "the vanishing wax cast." Thus Leonardo became the first biologic worker to use an injection of a solidifying medium to demonstrate the shape and size of a body cavity. The shape thus revealed is an extremely accurate portrayal of the ventricles within the fixed brain of the ox. It bears a close resemblance to the same spaces within the brain of man. He traced the vagus nerve to the floor of the third ventricle and then, because he found that the peripheral end of the left branch of the vagus nerve runs to the heart, Leonardo concluded that this area in the floor of the third ventricle controls the heart and that therefore it and not the heart is the seat of the soul.[53]

Leonardo beautifully portrayed the cranial nerves. He included the olfactory as one of them, an innovation, and described all of the cranial nerves except the third, the trochlear, to the eye. He depicted the eye as moved by four muscles but did not make their nerve a cranial nerve. However, he did draw and describe the optic chiasma.[54]

Leonardo incorrectly drew the spinal cord as running the full length of the spinal canal and showed also incorrectly hollow structures which he regarded as nerves following the course of the vertebrals at each side of the spinal canal; the structures shown resemble vertebral arteries.[55]

An example of the care with which Leonardo worked out the distribution of certain of the peripheral nerves is

33

seen in his demonstration that the median nerve to the hand supplies the lateral two and one-half fingers, the ulnar nerve the medial two and one-half fingers. Thus he points out that if the fingers are crossed and if the adjoining surfaces of two crossed fingers, the nerve supply of which overlaps, is painfully stimulated, pain seems to occur in three areas instead of in the two points stimulated, a discovery which, used as a parlor trick, was particularly pleasing to Leonardo.[56]

The Eye

"Since the eye is the window of the soul, the latter is always in fear of being deprived of it. . . ."

Codex Atlanticus, 119 v. a.

In his studies of the eye[57] Leonardo places the lens in the center of the eye, a Galenic concept, but this arrangement is found also in the myopic ox, Leonardo's favorite animal for dissection. To study the eye Leonardo fixed it in egg-white, coagulating the entire structure by boiling. The eye was then "cut transversely." Probably the hard lens, which was difficult to cut, invariably slipped from its proper location during this type of study. Leonardo's knowledge of the action of lenses made him realize that the function of the lens was to focus the light, received by the eye, upon the retina, and that vision was not perceived within the structure of the lens itself as current authority dictated. The inevitable inversion of the image by its passage through a double convex lens troubled

Leonardo, and he tried to account for the fact that man does not see upside down by imaging a double inversion, the first inversion occurring as the light passes through the pupil as it does through the pinpoint aperture of a camera obscura and the second correcting re-inversion occurring as the light passed on through the lens to the retina; he projected this theory only to discard it after further study.[58]

The area in the retina responsible for visual acuity Leonardo erroneously located upon the nerve-head, strangely the retina's only blind spot, but he realized that the area of visual acuity is very small: "The eye has one central line and all the things that come to the eye along this line are seen distinctly. Round about this line are an infinite number of lines close to this centre line, each having much less strength in proportion as it is more remote from the central line." This conclusion is reached through the observation that a slight change in position of the eye is needed to bring the periphery of an object into sharp focus, only the part seen directly as along a straight line being in sharp focus.[59]

Alimentary Organs

"The liver is the distributor and dispenser of vital nourishment to man. The bile is the familiar or servant of the liver. . . . The intestines: as to these you will understand their windings well if you inflate them. . . ."

35

Leonardo correctly described the action of swallowing and the correct course of a bolus of food as it passed over the larynx into the esophagus.

Although Leonardo's drawing of stomach and bowel, of the omentum and the spleen and liver, are quite clear, his understanding of the gastrointestinal tract is marred by his failure to note the intrinsic muscles of the bowel wall. The onward movement of the intestinal content he attributed to the action of the diaphragm and of the abdominal wall. (Not only did Leonardo fail to imagine peristalsis in the bowel; it escaped him also in the less obvious ureter.) Reflex of the material within the bowel he believed is prevented by the kinks and the gyrations of the bowel itself. He sees, draws, and describes the appendix,—the first appearance of this organ in any drawing in recorded history,—and makes conjecture as to its function, surmising that by its expansion it helps to relieve the pressure of gasses within the bowel. A characteristic anterior-posterior view of ascending, transverse, and descending colon, sigmoid, and rectum is shown twice, once with and once without diverticula. The picture containing diverticula probably represents the bowel of the old man whose body Leonardo so thoroughly studied.[60]

Evaluation

"Say on, Sandro! How does it strike you? I tell you what is true, and I have not made a success of it."   *Codex Atlanticus,* 313 r. b.

"Tell me if anything similar was ever made:

you understand and that is enough for the present."

Quaderni IV, 15 v.

Sources of knowledge in Leonardo's day and the contemporary levels of achievement are hard to arrive at because, in the presentation of an idea, the modern habit of clear formulation, with precise definition of terms and exact attribution to previous authorities, had not yet become the usual method of scientific presentation. Hence we assume priority for Leonardo when other prior sources of the data presented by him cannot be found. His own notebooks only casually credit sources for his material and this they do rarely.

The accumulated record of Leonardo's work is so overwhelming in amount that many early historians felt it must have more truly mirrored his times than to have been a record of new accomplishment. However, as a true evaluation of Leonardo's period becomes increasingly possible, we are constantly more impressed with the originality of Leonardo's anatomic and physiologic researches. The tragedy of their long neglect in his own century when a wide knowledge of Leonardo's work would have done the most good in stimulating the advance of science was due in great part to the inertia of his heir, Francesco Melzi. Melzi's only use of this vast material during the fifty years of life remaining to him after Leonardo's death was the compilation of a few selected paragraphs into a manuscript of the treatise on painting.[61]

Yet the record shows that Leonardo's drawings were

not entirely hidden to his contemporaries. While they were in the hands of Melzi they were seen and described by Anonimo Gaddiano; by Giorgio Vasari, who, probably in error, linked for the first time Leonardo's name to that of Marcantonio della Torre; and by the Milanese painter Gian Paolo Lomazzo, who tells in his *Idea del Tempio della Pittura*[62] of Leonardo's divinely drawn anatomical studies. Albrecht Dürer must have seen them when traveling in Italy, because he carefully copied some of the principal figures now in Windsor Castle into his *Dresden Sketchbook*.

However, it does not seem probable that Vesalius knew Leonardo's work in anatomy. How great would the benefit to the world have been if the towering genius of Vesalius could have stood on the shoulders of Leonardo instead of beside this earlier giant!

Amazement at the beauty and value of Leonardo's achievement is expressed by all the early writers who saw his work, but the real study of his great art and consummate science is left to our own time in which, through the combined art of the photoengraver and the printer and the devotion of historical and philological scholars, we are now only coming into a realization of the breadth and magnitude of Leonardo's concepts.

II

Leonardo da Vinci's Studies of the Genito-Urinary System

II. Leonardo da Vinci's Studies of the Genito-Urinary System

In Weimar, among the precious possessions of its Schlossmuseum, there is a single leaf of anatomic drawings which may have strayed from the larger collection of Leonardo da Vinci's drawings of anatomy now in Windsor Castle. Both sides of this Weimar leaf reveal many of Leonardo's concepts of the urinary and genital tracts.

In the age of Leonardo no artist drew faithfully any human structure deeper than the first layer of muscles beneath the skin. Anatomists were still overwhelmed with the immensity of Galen's knowledge. They almost deified his name, seldom venturing to differ from his concepts, indeed memorizing Galen rather than dissecting. In this period when anatomy was static it is almost miraculous to find these thrilling original anatomic studies of Leonardo da Vinci, filled with exciting new discoveries fresh from the dissecting room, made swiftly in the silence of the night upon the fast-decomposing human body.

That side of this Weimar leaf[1] which presents the torso of the female figure demonstrates the uterus, probably in early pregnancy. The great uterine vessels are spread upon its surface and an insert, presented in detail below, reveals one of the sources of the blood supply of the bladder. The ovaries lie on each side of the uterus; their ducts enter it near the cervix. Their veins empty on the left into the renal vein, on the right into the vena cava. Round liga-

41

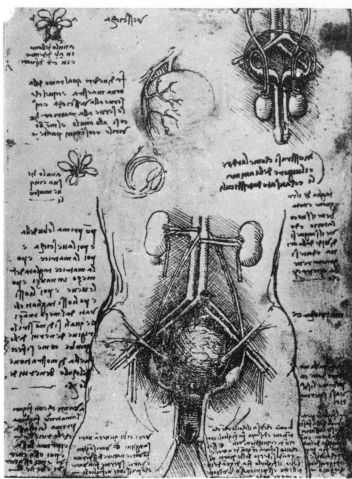

Anatomic drawing at the Schlossmuseum, Weimar, featuring male and female genitalia.

ments leave each uterine cornu to vanish into the inguinal regions. The vagina is a simple tube with the cervix in its vault. The kidneys are shown, vein, artery, and ureter in proper relation, the vessels branching as they do in man. The right kidney is erroneously higher than the left. The ureters leave the kidney and course downward but are shown only in their upper third. The lower ends of the ureters and the bladder have been removed to reveal the genital structures. In the upper left of this page are two trial drawings of a suggested but erroneous arrangement of the rectal sphincter muscles. In the upper right corner is a revealing sketch of the male genitalia. Here, as in the female figure, the organs are presented from the anteroposterior view. The urethra is laid open throughout its length. The ejaculatory ducts enter it at the bladder neck. The bladder is indicated as a transparency, represented by a circular ring. The drawing runs off the upper margin of the page; hence the origin of the testicular vessels is not seen, but these enter the right upper pole of each testis in a circular spiral. From this point also the vas deferens arises on each side. These vasa pass upward, running alongside the bladder to enter the superior tapering end of each seminal vesicle. Iliac veins and arteries, the vena cava and its bifurcation, and the aorta are seen beyond and behind the genital apparatus. In slightly greater detail this apparatus is also seen from the same aspect on the reverse side of the sheet.[2] Here the ejaculatory ducts are more clearly shown as they enter the uretha well beyond the bladder neck. These ducts arise from the

43

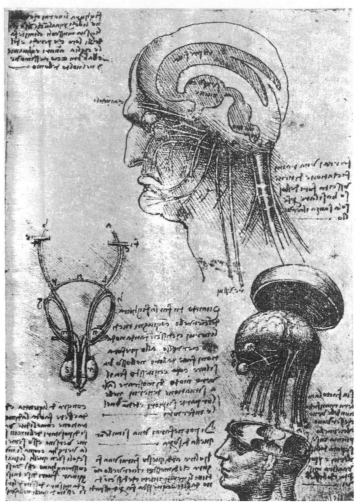

Anatomic drawing at the Schlossmuseum, Weimar, the reverse of the preceding figure.

44

seminal vesicles. Both the blood supply and the vasa deferentia merge into the apex of the seminal vesicles. Artery and vein of the testes run upward through the diagrammatically represented inguinal rings. In these drawings the canal through the penis is demonstrated as a single passage, not a double one as described by Galen. The bladder is circular, its urachus buds from its superior border, and the ureters cross its inferior lateral margins to pass into it.

The striking figures of the head and brain account for all of the cranial nerves except the trochlear and also clearly show the brain's ventricles demonstrated by Leonardo by means of solidifying hot wax. As students of the urinary tract, we are drawn to these figures of the brain and spinal cord by two fanciful structures which Leonardo demonstrates as passing parallel to the spinal cord, one on each side, seemingly arising from the substance of the brain. These were probably vertebral arteries, but in Leonardo's coition figure[3] we see them again, this time taking off from the lower end of the spinal canal. They were thought to carry spiritual power to the superior of two channels through the penis to contribute the more gummy portion of the ejaculate. Leonardo states: "With great diligence you should make the demonstration of the two vessels which are the depository of the human semen in the penis. Determine which structures are those which constrict these vessels and throw forth the semen. Give the measure and the site of those [structures] in the penis."[2]

This search follows the lead of the notion which came down from Hippocratic times that the most active and thickest part of the semen comes from the spinal cord and passes by means of vessels from the lumbar region to the testis. Though Leonardo presents this idea in his coition figure, actually he accepts the Galenical theory that sperm are made from blood within the structure of the testes. Convincing as this coition figure is, in it the student will discover many more errors than are revealed in the simple, clear, diagram-like sketches of the Weimar sheet from the Schlossmuseum. In the earlier coition figure it is interesting to follow the structure which takes off from the fundus of the uterus and passes on to the nipple. Through this vessel, according to authority, the retained menses of the pregnant female were thought to reach the breasts, where they were converted into milk. Leonardo's portentous warning written upon this coition drawing is: "In this way ulcers and disease may result."

The scattered notes written beside the figures on the Weimar leaf's torso page are a curious mixture of directions for further study, anatomic observations, and medical notions, some of which were current in Leonardo's day but some his own revolutionary thoughts. Beginning these legends with the script placed below the sketch of the male generative organs and running clockwise around the page they are:

"Show how the ardour and vigour of the animals is caused by the testicles." — "Cut the kidney and note well

46

its filtration and where the blood separates from the urine and where originates the gravel and the stone and why." — "uterus" — "Observe in the uterus where its spermatic vessels originate. The child generated by the fastidious lust of the woman and not of the will of the husband will be of small, vile and crude spirit."—"The man who uses coitus with contention and with depreciation makes irritable and untrustworthy children and when the coitus is made with great love and great desire of the partners then the child will be of great intellect, spirited and lively and lovable." — "Different food produces different blood and different blood makes different kind of sperm and different sperm have different influences on the children." — "Before you represent the uterus show first the case [i.e., pelvis] in which its connective tissue is contained and first the bones and then the bones and nerves and then the bones, nerves and veins." — "Put down first the intestine and then the bladder, then the uterus, then the uterus cut from the middle to the front, then the veins, then the bones and then the bones cut and lifted out from the middle to outside. In this should be shown the origin of the nerves of the legs as was done in the demonstration of the top of the nerves of the arms." — "The anus and its five muscles." — "Make visible which branch of the main vein it is which serves the bladder, also which one serves the uterus so with the uterus, the anus, the male member and thus all the parts." — "The anus of man in a-b from inside and c-d from outside." — "Bladder."

47

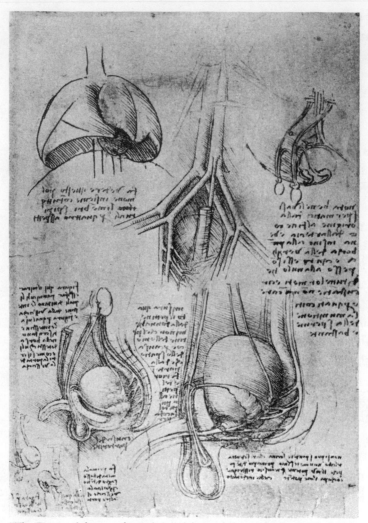

"The Ductus deferentes from their origin to their termination." "A demonstration of how the gateway of the bladder is closed." *Qu. III*, 4 r.

48

Lateral views of the pelvic viscera and genito-urinary tracts in the male are represented in a series of beautiful clarifying drawings in *Quaderni III,* 4 v. Here the urethra is shown as a single channel. Into it the ejaculatory ducts from the seminal vesicles empty beyond the sphincter fibers of the bladder neck. This relationship of ejaculatory ducts to internal sphincter of the bladder is shown in four little sketches, *Quaderni III,* 11 v., which represent the internal sphincter as a circle. The ejaculatory ducts are seen to enter the urethra quite distal to this circle. Discussing this point Leonardo says: "See which is the first in the urinary canal [urethra], either the mouths of the spermatic vessels [ejaculatory ducts] or the mouth of the urinary vessel [bladder]. But I believe that that of the urine is first so that it can then clean and wash out the sperm which makes the urinary canal sticky."[4]

The blood supply and vas deferens are seen passing through the inguinal canal. At this point the blood vessels pass upward toward the kidney and the ductus deferentes pass alongside the bladder to the seminal vesicles. The multiple blood supply to the overlarge bladder is clearly shown. Leonardo remarks: "Show the peritoneal membranes which separate the intestines from the bladder and demonstrate by what way the intestines descend into the sac of the testicles and how the gateway of the bladder is closed."[5]

A thrilling sketch of this gateway or bladder neck is demonstrated in a transverse section of the floor of the

49

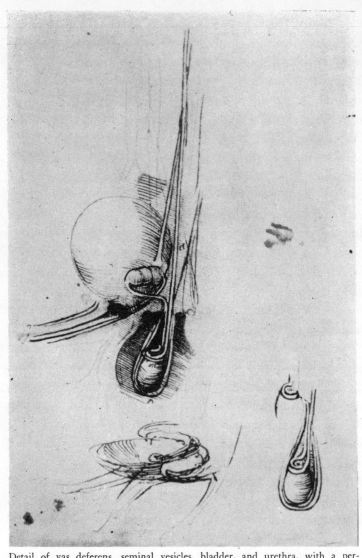

Detail of vas deferens, seminal vesicles, bladder, and urethra, with a perspective sketch of the bladder floor and bladder neck. *Qu. III*, 6 r.

bladder[6] illustrating clearly Leonardo's concept of the relations of bladder, bladder neck, urethra, and seminal apparatus. It is strange that the prostate is not shown in any of Leonardo's drawings. This may be due to the fact that most of his anatomic studies were made on the readily available bodies of oxen. These animals are castrates and have small atrophic prostates. In the rapidly degenerating bodies of his human subjects detailed dissection and study were less easily carried out and bodies for dissection were hard to obtain. Leonardo often transposes knowledge gained from his animal dissections directly into his figures which purport to present the anatomy of man. As M. F. Ashley Montagu says in reference to Galen: "Where he erred was in his tendency to extrapolate, to transfer without checking, his findings on one animal to the structure of a totally different one. Thus, the details of many structures observed by Galen in pigs, monkeys, and other animals· are by him described as normal structures in man."[7]

A lateral view of the female generative system is seen in *Quaderni III, 1 v.* Here the ovary receives its blood supply as does the testis in the male. Ovarian ducts join the uterus; the kidneys, ureters, and very large bladder are well shown. As in the beautiful Weimar leaf, the body of the uterus and the cervix with the cervical os are readily recognizable.

A view of the uterus from the anteroposterior position is shown at the top of this same page. The cervical os is seen. The cavity of the uterus is single, contrary to author-

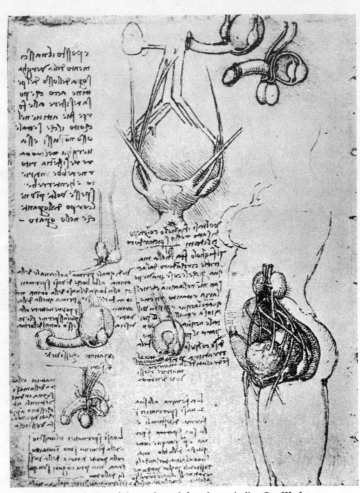

Homologies of the male and female genitalia. *Qu. III*, 1 v.

52

ity. The ovaries with their oviducts leading into the uterus lie at each side of the uterus. On the right, the blood supply of the ovary is seen to be derived from aorta and vena cava. The course of the vessels belonging to the left ovary is not completed in the drawing. Of the two additional structures emerging from the uterine cornu, one is a representation of what is probably the round ligament. The other is the duct indicated in the coition figure, thought to extend to the breasts. It is noteworthy that this fictional structure does not appear in the more advanced observations shown in the Weimar leaf.

Other diagrammatic figures on this page attempt to illustrate the homologies between the two sexes, a favorite subject for argument carried on from the time of Galen. In Leonardo's judgment the male urethra is the homologue of the vagina, the seminal vesicles are the homologue of the uterus, the testes are the homologues of the ovaries, the ductus deferentes are homologous to the vas seminarium or suspensory ligament of the ovary, and spermatic vessels are homologous to the ovarian vessels.

Leonardo's attempt at functional approaches to anatomic problems is illustrated by his remarks on the penis: "The origin of the penis is situated upon the pubic bone so that it can resist its active force on coition. If this bone did not exist, the penis in meeting resistance would turn backward and would often enter more into the body of the operator than into that of the operated."[8]

The erectile power of the penis had been attributed

by the ancients to a pneuma, or vital spirit. In the Middle Ages this thought had become corrupted into the idea that air under pressure produced the hardness of the penis and indeed the hardness of muscles under exertion was also attributed to such an effect. Leonardo knew much about the action of air under pressure. His invention of a submarine for war purposes is clearly stated and must have depended upon air compressed into cylinders. He carefully kept secret the basic principles of this invention, explaining that he destroyed these records because of the possible harm to mankind of such a device in war. It is strange that thoughts of harm to mankind in war from his airship did not seem to enter his mind. Air pressure and the fact that air under compression tended to become solid enough to lift weights is clearly expressed in this statement of the first principle of aeronautics: "The movement of the air against a fixed thing is as great as the movement of the movable thing against the air which is immovable."[9]

So we are not surprised to see Leonardo presenting arguments based on the physical properties of air to overcome these prevailing notions in regard to the reason for the hardness of muscles under exertion and the hardness of the penis in erection. He states: .

What is it that increases the size of the muscles so rapidly? It is said that it is air [pneuma]—and where does it go when the muscle diminishes with such rapidity? Into the nerves of sensibility which are hollow? Indeed, that would be a vast amount of air, that which enlarges and elongates the penis and makes it as dense as wood, so that the whole great quantity of air [in the nerves] would not be sufficient for reduction to such a density; not only the air of the nerves, but if the body were filled with it, it would not suffice. If you will have it that it is the air of these nerves, what air is it that courses through the muscles and reduces them to such hardness and power at the time of the carnal act? For I once saw a mule which was almost unable to move, owing to the fatigue of a long journey under a heavy burden, and which, on seeing a mare, suddenly its penis and all its muscles became so turgid that it multiplied its forces as to acquire such speed that it overtook the course of the mare which fled before it and which was obliged to obey the desires of the mule.[10]

Having dealt with "pneuma" as a factor in erections he substitutes his theory of blood under pressure as a cause for this phenomenon:

Of the virile member when it is hard, it is thick and long, dense and heavy, and when it is limp, it is thin, short and soft, that is, limp and weak. This should not be adjudged as due to the addition of flesh or wind, but to arterial blood. I have seen this in the dead who have this member rigid. For many die thus, especially those hanged of whom I have seen an anatomy, having great density and hardness, and these are full of a large quantity of blood which has made the flesh very red within, and in others, without as well as within. And if an opponent contends that this large amount of flesh has grown through wind which causes the enlargement and hardness as in a ball with which we play, this wind provides neither weight nor density but makes the flesh light and rarefied. And again, one observes that the rigid penis has a red glans [*testa*] which is a sign of an abundance of blood, and when it is not rigid, it has a whitish appearance.[11]

The Italian humanist Poggio had discovered a manuscript of the *De Rerum Natura* of Lucretius[12] in which it was stated that the foetus "is always fashioned out of the two seeds," male and female. It is upon this point that Leonardo takes the author of one of his important source books to task, addressing him as if he were an adversary in debate: "It is you, Mundinus, who state that the 'spermatic vessels' or testicles [ovaries] do not excrete real semen but only a certain saliva-like humor which Nature has ordained for the delectation of women in coition, in which case, if it were so, it would not be necessary that origin of the spermatic vessels derive in the same way in the female as in the male."[13] Thus he makes inferences regarding function from structure, for in Leonardo's drawing of the blood supply of ovaries and testes the asymmetry of the right and left sides is almost always demonstrated. The veins from the left testis and ovary are shown uniting with the renal vein, and those from the right enter the vena cava.[14]

Continuing on the theme of ovarian function, Leonardo states: "The female has her 2 spermatic vessels in the shape of the testicles [i.e., ovaries with suspensory ligaments], and her sperm is at first blood like that of the male. But when one inseminates the other, the testicles receive the generative faculty but not one without the other. Neither one [ovum] nor the other [sperm] is preserved in the testicles [used in common for ovary and testes] but one is preserved in the womb and the other, that of the male, is preserved in the two ventricles *a b* [seminal vesicles], which are attached behind the bladder."[15]

Leonardo's reasoning in regard to the distribution of heredity factors between male and female parent in the offspring is shown in his statement regarding cross breeding between black and white races of men: "The black races in Ethopia are not the product of the sun; for if black gets black with child in Scythia, the offspring is black; but if a black gets a white woman with child. the offspring is grey. And this shows that the seed of the mother has power in the embryo equally with that of the father."[16]

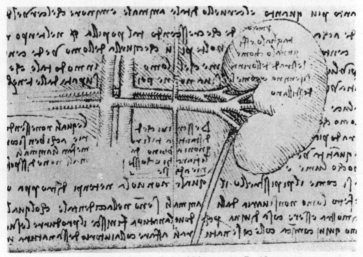

External form of the kidney. *An. B*, 13 v.

Although Leonardo clearly represents the outward form of the kidney, the correct relationship of the renal artery, vein, and ureter, and demonstrates also the entry of the left spermatic vein into the left renal vein and of the right spermatic vein[17] into the vena cava (an observation also recorded by Galen), we find in Leonardo no demonstrations of the interior of the kidney. There are several notes reminding himself to make such an investigation similar to the one quoted from the Weimar sheet above. One of these is written on the kidney shown in *An. B,* 13 v. Here we find the statement: "Cut it through the middle and depict how the passages for the urine are closed and how they distill it."

Considerable insight into renal function is shown in Leonardo's reference to salt. Noting the bags of salt being carried into the cities, he says: "The human species has eternally been and will be consumers of salt. This salt must pass through the bodies of men either in the urine or the sweat." Leonardo has noted that salt is not metabolized or changed in use.[18]

It is especially interesting to see Leonardo's struggle to understand the passage of the urine from the kidney into the bladder through the ureter. The motile peristaltic activity of the ureter is unknown to him. He treats the ureter as if it were a simple tube; the water flowing through it, in his mind, is influenced only by gravity and by those laws which control the flow of liquids. Hence his interesting comments:

The urine, having left the kidneys, enters the ureters and from there passes into the bladder near the middle of its height. It enters the bladder through minute perforations made transversely between tunic and tunic. This oblique perforation was not made because Nature doubted that the urine could return to the kidneys, for that is impossible from the 4th [book] on conduits where it is stated: water which descends from above through a narrow vessel and enters under the bottom of a pool, cannot be opposed by reflux movement if the magnitude of the water in the pool is not as great as the magnitude of the vessel which descends, or the height of the water greater than the depth of the pool. If you were to say that the more the bladder is filled the more it closes, to this I should reply that these perforations being compressed by the urine which closes the wall, would prevent the entrance of other urine which descends. This cannot be according to the 4th [book] mentioned above which states that the narrow and elevated [stream of] urine is more powerful than the low and wide which lies in the bladder.[19]

The detail of the ureterovesical valve, Leonardo's "oblique perforation," carefully drawn in the figures presented through the upward turn of the intramural portion of the ureter, is certainly not human in structure. The lateral picture of the bladder which shows the blood vessels of the bladder wall and their relation to the point of entry of the ureter into the bladder reveals very nicely the little artery which always encircles the ureter at this point.

The study of the flow of urine through the ureters into the bladder is carried further in *An. B,* 14 r. There the

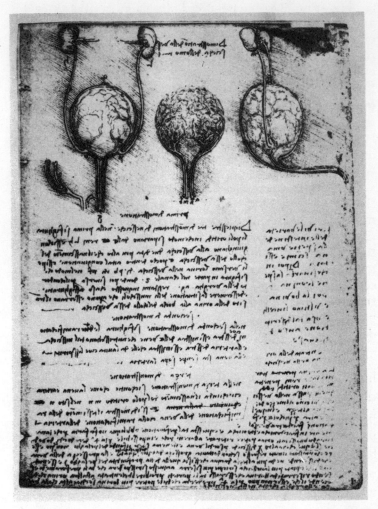

Relation of ureters to kidney and bladder. Detail of the ureterovesical juncture.
An. B, 37 r.

effect of position upon urine drainage from kidney to bladder is illustrated in a series of diagrammatic sketches which show the patient (1) erect, (2) upside down, and (3) lying on his side. The argument runs:

The authorities say that the ureters in carrying urine to the bladder do not enter it directly but enter between layer and layer in such a way that they are not opposed, and that the more the bladder is filled, the more they are closed. They say that Nature has done this solely because when the bladder is full, it would return the urine back whence it came. Hence on finding its way between membrane and membrane to enter the interior [of the bladder] through a narrow passage not corresponding to [the point of entry in] the first membrane, the more the bladder is filled, the more it forces one membrane against the other, and thus has no cause to reverse and turn back. This proof is not true for the reason that if the urine in the bladder were to rise higher than its entrance, which is near the middle of its height, it would follow that this entrance would be closed immediately, and it would be impossible for more urine to enter the bladder, and it would never exceed half the capacity of the bladder. Therefore, the rest of the bladder would be superfluous, and Nature makes nothing superfluous. Consequently, we shall state, according to the 5th [section] of the 6th [book] "On water," how the urine enters through a long and tortuous passage into the bladder and then when the bladder is full, the ureters remain full of urine. The urine of the bladder cannot rise higher than their surfaces [of the intramural portion of the ureters] when man is standing erect. But if he remains lying down, it can return back through the ureters and even more so, if he places himself upside down, which occurs infrequently, although recumbency is common. Whereas if a man lies upon his side, one of the ureters remains above, the other below, and the entrance of that above opens and discharges the urine into the bladder. The other duct below closes because of the weight of the urine. Hence a single duct gives its urine to the bladder, and it is sufficient that one of the emulgent [renal] veins purifies the blood of the urinary chyle mixed with it, since the emulgent veins are opposite one another and do not proceed entirely from the vena chilis [vena cava]. [In other words, the kidneys need not operate simultaneously but one kidney can very well function at a time.] And if a man lies with his back to the sky, the 2 ureters pour urine into the bladder. They enter through the upper part of the bladder [when prone], since the ducts are attached to the posterior part of the bladder, the part which when the body is lying downwards, remains above. Thus the urinary entrances can remain open and contribute to the bladder as much urine as required to fill it.[20]

Such statements would possibly hold true if the ureter were a simple tube without propulsive power of its own, but they are certainly not true of the living functioning ureter equipped, through peristalsis, with sufficient power to propel the urine onward even into an overfilled bladder.

The magnitude of Leonardo's ambition for his projected anatomy is shown in the intricate *Situs* drawing. With this figure Leonardo begins his intended series of graphic presentations and states: "Also make this demonstration as seen from the side so that knowledge may be given how far one part lies behind the other. Then make

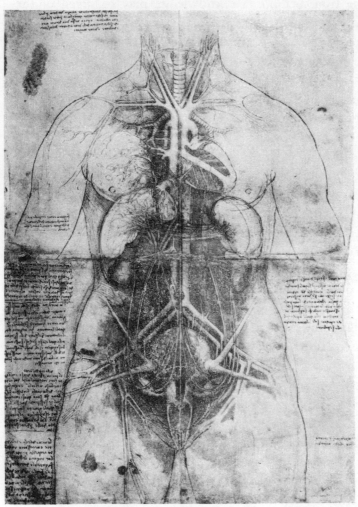

The great *Situs* figure. *Qu. I,* 12 r.

one from behind that knowledge may be given of the veins possessed by the spine and by the heart, and of the greater vessels." He adds: "Your series shall be with the beginning of the formation of the child in the womb, stating which part of it is formed first, and so successively putting in its part according to the periods of pregnancy until birth and how it is nourished, learning partly from the eggs laid by hens."

This *Situs* drawing presents a mixture of traditional notions and accurate observation. The heart is the two-chambered heart of the ancients with a thick ventricle and, as in the ox, moderator bands in both ventricles. The vena cava opens directly into the right ventricle. The branchings of the aorta are similar to those of the ox. The large, possibly pregnant uterus has a single cavity, but the scalloped edges of this cavity are remnants of the seven cells of Michael Scott brought down to Leonardo through Mundinus, seen in Guy de Vigevano, and published in Leonardo's own day by Magnus Hundt.[21]

The tubular structures seen to emerge from the lateral walls of the uterus are the uterine cornu of earlier authorities. The long wandering blood vessels carrying the retained menses of the pregnant woman from the uterus to the breast for the manufacture of milk are also shown.

Yet even with its many throwbacks to Galenic authority, Leonardo's demonstration represents an astonishing advance when compared with illustrations current in his day, such as are shown in Magnus Hundt's contemporary book, printed in 1501. With his *Situs* figure as a start, reflecting so many medieval concepts, Leonardo was soon to advance into a myriad of new observations in all of the systems which his dissections laid bare. It is little wonder that with his almost daily excursions into the world of the unknown Leonardo was unable to crystallize his thoughts into copy for printed presentation; so his great work remained as laboratory notes only. However, these notes, because of the very fact that they are unedited, show us the first flash of inspiration, retaining the power and strength of original observation and discovery.

In Leonardo's written text, augmented by his demonstrations through drawings, we see his firm convictions that the contributions of the male and female parent to heredity are equal; that the testes and ovaries have a similar blood supply and therefore a similar function; that the testes and the ovaries build their sex cells from the blood, the testes passing on their secretion to the seminal vesicles which hold it for ejaculation (previous authority had held that a portion at least of the ejaculate was contributed from the spinal canal); that the ovaries also create their sex cells from the blood, passing them on through ducts to the cavity of the uterus; that the uterus has a single cavity and not seven or eight as taught by Michael Scott; that erections are caused not by compressed air forced into the body of the penis but by engorgement of this organ with blood under pressure; that venery is a source of disease; that the ureters pass obliquely through the bladder

65

wall; that the intestines descend along the spermatic vessels through a peritoneal lined canal to produce herniae; that the ejaculatory ducts enter the urethra peripheral to the internal sphincter of the bladder.

Leonardo was the first artist who is known to have advanced beyond the anatomy of flayed bodies and to have carried his studies into the deeper muscles and thoracic and abdominal viscera. Fortune combined in him the abilities of a graphic artist of the greatest powers, an infinite scientific curiosity, and a phenomenal ability to analyze his experiences. He developed through these powers an understanding of natural forces far beyond others of the stirring age in which he lived.

Leonardo's anatomic studies, therefore, as Charles O'Malley says, show a curious mixture of the traditional ignorance current in his day and a knowledge beyond his time acquired from experience in dissection. There is always evident a composite of medieval tradition and of human and animal dissection. In his ideas he moves onward from a debased medieval Aristotelianism through a corrupt Galenism to relative scientific independence. It is a joy to see his progress from schematic designs made to illustrate the wordy descriptions of Mundinus and Avicenna to later scientific anatomic drawings of his own made from his observations, accurately portraying the material he saw and dissected.

In his drawings Leonardo reaches the greatest heights of artistic anatomic portrayal. He states:

66

With what words, O writer, will you describe with like perfection the entire configuration which the drawing here does? Lacking knowledge, this you describe confusedly and leave little conception of the true shape of things while you, in self-deception, make believe that you can fully satisfy your auditors when you must speak of the configuration of some bodily structure bounded by surfaces. But I counsel you not to encumber yourself with words unless you are speaking to the blind. If, however, you wish to demonstrate in words to the ears and not to the eyes of men, speak of substantial or natural things and do not meddle with things appertaining to the eyes by making them enter through the ears, for you will be far surpassed by the work of the painter.[22]

Rachel Annand Taylor's beautiful sonnet pays fitting tribute to Leonardo the Anatomist, toiling alone in his nightly vigil of dissection:

Macabre beauty of the skeleton
    Endures his lonely inquest, head to foot:
Flexions, articulations, one by one
    He tries as sensitively as his lute.
The silverpoint states very preciously
    Pronation, supination, what you will:
Of bones like finely carved ivory
    It redes the riddle with a Chinese skill.
Like dahlia-flowers most implicate and rich
    The intimate clots of life he can expose,
Even the poor heart, so vulnerable, which
    He draws as delicately as a rose—
Then, smiling, lets his sinister hand unglove,
    Startling, bizarre, the Anatomy of Love.[23]

67

Notes

ABBREVIATIONS

An. A — Dell' Anatomia Fogli A, Paris, Rouveyre 1, 1898.
An. B — Dell' Anatomia Fogli B, Torino, Roux e Viarengo, 1901.
Cod. Atl.—Codex Atlanticus, Milan, Hoepli, 1894-1904.
MS. D — *Les Manuscrits B & D de la Bibliothèque de l'Institut de France,* Paris, Ravaisson-Mollien, 1883.
Qu. I - VI Quaderni d'Anatomia, Christiania, J. Dybwad, 1911-1916.

I

Note: The first lecture is based largely on Elmer Belt, *"Les dissections anatomiques de Léonard de Vinci,"* in *Léonard de Vinci et l'expérience scientifique au XVIe siècle,* 4-7 juillet, 1952. Paris, *Colloque International, Centre National de la Recherche Scientifique.* 1953.

1. Giorgio Vasari, *Le Vite de' piu Eccellenti Pittori, Scultori ed Architettori,* a cura di G. Milanesi, Florence, Sansoni, 1906.

2. *An. A,* 16 r. and v. *Qu. I,* 2 r.

3. Luca Beltrami, *Documenti. . .,* Milano, Fr. Treves, 1919, p. 149.

4. Edmondo Solmi, *"Le fonti dei manoscritti di Leonardo da Vinci,"* *Giornale della Letteratura Italiana,* Torino, 1908, pp. 3 and 21 ff.

5. *An. B,* 10 v.

6. Cod. Atl., 182 v.

7. *Qu. I,* 13 v.

8. Luca Pacioli, *Divina proportione,* Venice, 1509, and *Quellenschriften fuer Kunstgeschichte und Kunsttechnik. . .,* Neue Folge, Band II, ed. Constantin Winterberg, Vienna, C. Graeser, 1889.

9. Jean Paul Richter, *The Literary Works of Leonardo da Vinci,* London, New York, Oxford University Press, 1939, Vol. II, p. 394; Elmer Belt, *Manuscripts of Leonardo da Vinci,* Los Angeles, California, The Ward Ritchie Press, 1948, p. 8.

10. Roger de Piles, *Abrégé de la Vie des Peintres,* Paris, F. Muguet, 1699, pp. 166 ff.

11. Enrico Carusi, *Lettere di Galeazzo Arconati e Cassiano del Pozzo,* Accademic e b:blioteche d'Italia, 1929, Vol. III, p. 6.

12. John Chaimberlaine, *Imitations of Original Designs by Leonardo da Vinci . . . in His Majesty's Collection,* London, Bulmer, 1796, p. 10.

13. William Hunter, *Uteri humani gravidi tabulis illustra,* London, Baskerville, 1774, Introduction.

14. J. F. Blumenbach, *Von den anatomischen Zeichnungen des Leonardo da Vinci . . .,* Medizinische Bibliothek, Goettingen, Dietrich, 1788.

15. Charles O'Malley and J. B. de C. M. Saunders, *Leonardo da Vinci on the Human Body,* New York, Schuman, 1952.

16. Emil Moeller, *Abbozzi e testi sconosciuti del Vinci sull' anatomia;* Milano, Raccolta Vinciana XIII, Supplemento, 1913.

17. *Qu. I,* 2 r.

18. *Qu. V,* 21 r.

19. *An. A,* 8 v.

20. *An. B*, 41 v.
21. *An. A*, 1 v.
22. *An. B*, 41 v.
23. Kenneth Clark, *A Catalogue of the Drawings of Leonardo da Vinci*, Cambridge, The University Press, 1935, pp. xxi, xxx.
24. *Qu. V*, 4 r.
25. *Qu. V*, 3 v.
26. *Ibid.*
27. *Qu. V*, 19 r. and 20 r.
28. *An. A*, 1 f. to 2 r. and 3 v. to 4 v.
29. *Qu. II*, 12 r.
30. *Qu. V*, 22 r.
31. *Qu. V*, 11 r.
32. *Qu. IV*, 1 v.
33. *An. A*, 3 r.
34. *Qu. III*, 8 r.
35. *Qu. V*, 21 r.
36. *An. A*, 3 r.
37. *Qu. I*, 6 r.
38. *An. A*, 8 v., 9 r., *An. B*, 40 r. and v., 42 r. *et passim.*
39. *An. A*, 13 v.
40. *An. B*, 29 r.
41. *An. B*, 27 r.
42. *An. A*, 1 v.
43. MS. D, *Of the Eye.*
44. *Qu. II*, various demonstrations.
45. *Qu. II*, 1 r. to 23 r., *Qu. IV*, 13 r., *An. B*, 12 r.
46-48. *An. B*, 10 r. and v., 22 r. and v.; Elmer Belt, "Leonardo da Vinci's Studies of the Aging Process," *Geriatrics*, Vol. VII, June, 1952, p. 3.
49. *An. B*, 33 v.
50. *An. B*, 27 v., 37 v., 17 r.
51. *An. B*, 28 r.
52. *Qu. V*, 6 v., 7 r., 15 r., Weimar anatomical leaf.
53. *An. B*, 41 r.
54. *Qu. V*, 6 v. *An. B*, 35 r. Weimar anatomical leaf.
55. *Qu. III*, 3 r.
56. *An. B*, 8 v., *Qu. V*, 21 v.
57. MS. D, *Of the Eye*, especially f. 8 v.
58. *Ibid.*
59. *Ibid.*
60. *An. B*, 14 r. and v., 22 v.
61. Codex Vaticanus (Urbinas) 1270, first printed in an abbreviated version in Paris, Langlois, 1651.
62. Gian Paolo Lomazzo, *Idea del Tempio della Pittura*, Milano, Gortrado da Pontio, 1590.

II

1. Anatomic leaf, Weimar, Schlossmuseum. Width: upper margin 13.7 cm., lower margin 14 cm. Height: left margin 19 cm., right margin 19.3 cm.

Pen and ink, bister. Since 1910 traceable in the Schlossmuseum. Provenance not certain; probably from the collection of William, King of Holland, from whence it came by inheritance to the King's daughter Sophia, Grand Duchess of Sachsen-Weimar. See Emil Moeller, *Abbozzi e testi sconosciuti* . . ., Milano, Raccolta Vinciana XIII, supplemento, 1913.

2. *Ibid.*

3. *Qu. III*, 3 v.

4. *Qu. III*, 1 v.

5. *Qu. III*, 4 v.

6. *Qu. III*, 6 r.

7. M. F. Ashley Montagu, "Vesalius and the Galenists" in *Science, Medicine and History, Essays . . . Written in Honor of Charles Singer*, London and New York, Oxford University Press, 1953, Vol. I, p. 380.

8. *Qu. III*, 1 v.

9. Cod. Atl., 395 r. - b.

10. *An. A*, 18 r.

11. *An. B*, 2 v.

12. Charles D. O'Malley and J. B. de C. M. Saunders, *Leonardo da Vinci on the Human Body*, New York, Henry Schuman, 1952, p. 454 (plate 201; *Qu.* 3, 1 v.). For the quotations of Leonardo's text in general Charles D. O'Malley's new translation has been used with the permission of author and publisher. This translation surpasses in accuracy all previous translations done into English.

13. *Qu. I*, 12 r.

14. *Qu. III*, 10 v.; *An. B*, 13 v.; *Qu. III*, 5 r. *et passim.*

15. *Qu. III*, 1 v.

16. *Qu. III*, 8 v.

17. *Qu. I*, 12 r.; *Qu. III*, 5 r.

18. MS. G in the Institut de France, 48 r. and v.

19. *An. B*, 37 r.

20. *An. B*, 14 r.

21. Magnus Hundt, *Antropologium*, Leipzig, 1501, fol. L2r.

22. *Qu. II*, 1 r.

23. Rachel Annand Taylor, "Anatomical Studies," the fifth in a cycle of thirteen sonnets, *Adam, International Review*, London, 1952.

INDEX

(Subjects of illustrations are italicized.)

73